Oscar the Mighty

Written and Illustrated by
Chuck Gonzales

SCHOLASTIC INC.
New York Toronto London Auckland
Sydney New Delhi Hong Kong

Copyright © 2012 by Scholastic Inc.
All rights reserved. Published by Scholastic Inc.
Printed in the U.S.A.

ISBN-13: 978-0-545-34068-7
ISBN-10: 0-545-34068-3
(meets NASTA specifications)

4 5 6 7 8 9 10   113   20 19 18 17 16 15 14 13 12 11

Hey Oscar, nice catch! Use your nostril next time!

Why don't you use your mouth? It's big enough.

OSCAR GOMEZ LIVES IN A SMALL TOWN IN THE MIDWEST. IT'S A CUTE LITTLE TOWN. IT'S FULL OF TREES, NICE HOUSES, BIG YARDS AND WHITE PICKET FENCES.

Oscar! What happened to your nose?

Well mom, it's like this...

Here he goes again.

SCRAPE

In the heart of the Midwest prairie lands lives the mighty emperor, Oscar-tavious. His troops love him. His battle skills are amazing. His speeches are even better!!

Oscar-tavious was rallying the crowd. He was giving a great speech. Then suddenly... the sun came out of the sky. **WHAM!**

Okay, mighty one, what really happened?

Eric Olsen hit the ball really hard. As usual, he aimed for my face.

Oh Oscar! I'm sure Eric didn't hit you on purpose.

I'm going up to my room.

WELL, IT WASN'T *JUST* OSCAR'S ROOM. UNFORTUNATELY, HE HAD TO SHARE WITH HIS OLDER BROTHER, JUAN. AT SCHOOL OR AT HOME, LIFE WAS NEVER FAIR!

Well, hello, ERIC.

Here you go, pea brain.

Too bad your pal Sparhawk isn't here to protect you now!

Ooow Oscar, please NO! I didn't mean to make fun of youuuu!

There, you're as good as new. Let's go check out Tiffany's room!

EVEN ERIC DID NOT DESERVE TO BE LEFT WITH TIFFANY! OSCAR SNEAKED BACK TO RESCUE HIM.

Oooooooooow! Can't you see I'm already damaged?

You're damaged, all right...

OF COURSE, OSCAR COULD NOT HIDE THE THIRD PEA. JUAN AND TIFFANY JUST HAD TO SPOT IT.

Got him! Quick! The pea!

Don't let go. He'll bite my hand off!

GAG! GAG! ACK!

GAG ULP GAG

I think he swallowed it.

Dork boy!

Poot

NOW IT'S BEDTIME. OSCAR'S LIFE CONTINUES TO BE TOTALLY UNFAIR.

sigh

SIGH.

WHAT?

I can't sleep.

What's the matter?

I'm afraid of dying!

Everyone will die some day, Oscar. It's a part of the cycle.

What cycle? I don't even know how to ride a bike!

THE NEXT DAY, OSCAR'S CLASS GATHERED IN THE SCHOOL GYM. IT WAS TIME TO GET READY FOR THE FALL PLAY.

Let me guess. We're doing the first Thanksgiving again.

I hope I don't have to be the turkey again!

I had to be mashed potatoes last year. That was the worst.

OSCAR'S SCHOOL WAS SMALL. MANY TEACHERS HAD TWO JOBS. GUESS WHO DIRECTED THE CLASS PLAYS?

CUT

SPARHAWK

OSCAR ALREADY KNEW WHICH PART SHE'D GIVE HIM.

We are doing the first Thanksgiving, class. Oscar and Quinta will be a nice Native American couple.

OSCAR AND QUINTA ALWAYS HAD TO PLAY ANYONE WHO WAS NOT PALE AND WHITE! SOMETIMES THEY HAD TO BE A COUPLE! GROSS!

ULP

AGAIN?

What's the problem, Quinta? Oscar's sister, Tiffany, loved acting in plays. She made a lovely Pocahontas.

She just loved playing a princess!

18